BRYAN ADAMS

(Everything I Do) I Do It For You...
plus 13 Chart Hits arranged for piano, voice & guitar.

WISE PUBLICATIONS
London / New York / Sydney

Exclusive Distributors:

MUSIC SALES LIMITED
8/9 Frith Street,
London W1V 5TZ, England.

MUSIC SALES PTY LIMITED
120 Rothschild Avenue,
Rosebery, NSW 2018, Australia.

This book © Copyright 1992 by
Wise Publications.
Order No. AM89634
ISBN 0-7119-3050-3

Book design by Michael Bell Design.
Compiled by Peter Evans.
Photographs courtesy of Retna Limited.

Music Sales' complete catalogue
lists thousands of titles and is free
from your local music shop, or direct
from Music Sales Limited.
Please send a cheque/postal order
for £1.50 for postage to:
Music Sales Limited, Newmarket Road,
Bury St. Edmunds, Suffolk IP33 3YB.

Printed in the United Kingdom by
J.B. Offset Printers (Marks Tey) Limited,
Marks Tey, Essex.

SEAL

BRYAN ADAMS

JULEE CRUISE

BETTE MIDLER

KYLIE MINOGUE

WET WET WET

CURTIS STIGERS

EXTREME

GENESIS

ROD STEWART

ERIC CLAPTON

THE COMMITMENTS

DIANA ROSS

THE SCORPIONS

(Everything I Do) I Do It For You

Words & Music by Bryan Adams, Michael Kamen & Robert John 'Mutt' Lange.

you're there   all the   time, _____ all the   way ___ yeah. _____

Oh   you can't

tell   me   it's not   worth   try - in'   for,   I   can't

help _____ it,   there's   no - thin'   I   want   more.   Yeah ___ I   would

VERSE 2:
Look into your heart
You will find there's nothin' there to hide
Take me as I am, take my life
I would give it all, I would sacrifice.

Don't tell me it's not worth fightin' for
I can't help it, there's nothin' I want more
You know it's true, everything I do
I do it for you.

From A Distance

Words & Music by Julie Gold.

Lyrics:

From a dis-tance the world looks blue and green, and the snow-capped moun-tains so white. From a dis-tance the oc-ean meets the stream, and the ea-gle takes to flight. From a

watch-ing us __ from a dis - tance. _____

From a dis - tance you look __ like my friend, __ ev - en though __ we are __ at war. From a dis - tance I __ can't com-

More Than Words

Words & Music by Nuno Bettencourt & Gary Cherone.

Say-ing "I __ love __ you" is not the words __ I want to __ hear __ from you. __ It's not that I __ want __ you not to say, __ but if __

more __ than __ words.__

- ing "I __ love __ you."

D.S.

Now that I've tried to talk to you
And make you understand
All you have to do is close your eyes
And just reach out your hands
And touch me
Hold me close, don't ever let me go
More than words
Is all I ever needed you to show
Then you wouldn't have to say
That you love me
'Cause I'd already know.

Try A Little Tenderness

Words & Music by Harry Woods, Jimmy Campbell & Reg Connelly.

And when she's wea-ry, Try a lit-tle ten-der-ness.

You know she's wait-ing, Just an-ti-ci-pat-ing, Things she may nev-er poss-ess. While she's with-out them, Try a lit-tle ten-der-ness.

It's not just sen-ti-men-tal, She

has her grief and care,_____ And a word_____ that's soft and gen-tle, Makes it

ea-si-er to bear. You won't re-gret it, Wo-men don't for-get it,

Love is their whole hap-pi-ness. It's all so ea-sy Try a lit-tle ten-der-

a tempo

ness.

ness._____

rall.

opt: *D.S.*

Wind Of Change

Words & Music by Klaus Meine.

(1.) I fol-low the Mosk-ya down to Gor-ky Park.

lis-tening to the wind of change. An Au-gust sum-mer

night, sol-diers pass-ing by ___ lis-tening to the wind ___ of change.

CHORUS

Take me ___ to the ma-gic of the mo-ment on a glo-

-ry night, ___ where the chil-dren of to-mor-row 2,3.{Dream a - way
Share their dreams

in the wind of change.
with you and me.

Take me ___ to the ma-gic of the mo-ment on a glo-

Verse 2:

The world is closing in
Did you ever think
That we could be so close, like brothers
The future's in the air
I can feel it everywhere
Blowing with the wind of change.

Verse 3: D.S.

Walking down the street
Distant memories
Are buried in the past forever
I follow the Moskya
Down to Gorky Park
Listening to the wind of change.

Falling

Words & Music by Angelo Badalamenti & David Lynch.

Slowly, expressively

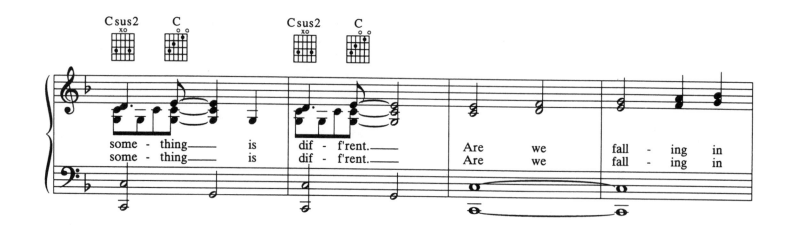

some - thing___ is dif - f'rent.___ Are we fall - ing in
some - thing___ is dif - f'rent.___ Are we fall - ing in

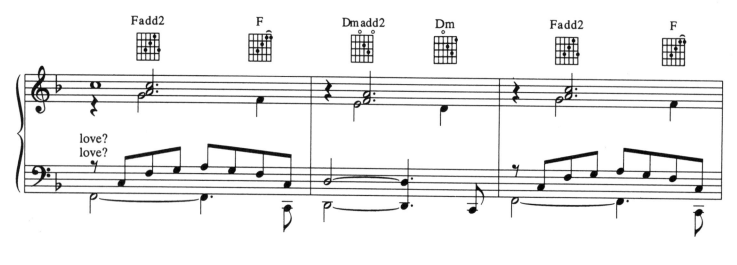

love?
love?

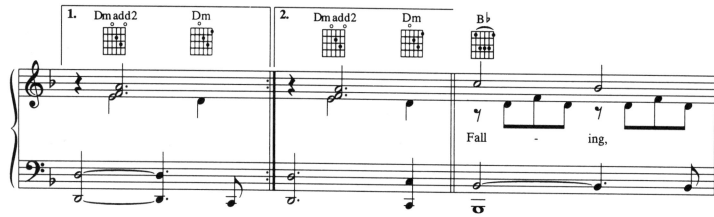

1. Dmadd2   Dm

2. Dmadd2   Dm   B♭

Fall - ing,

fall - ing,   fall - ing,   fall - ing in

Tears In Heaven

Words & Music by Eric Clapton & Will Jennings.

VERSE 2:
Would you hold my hand
If I saw you in heaven?
Would you help me stand
If I saw you in heaven?
I'll find my way
Through night and day,
'Cause I know I just can't stay
Here in heaven.

VERSE 3: (D.S.)

Instrumental solo — 8 bars

Beyond the door
There's peace, I'm sure;
And I know there'll be no more
Tears in heaven.

VERSE 4: (D.S.)
Would you know my name
If I saw you in heaven?
Would you be the same
If I saw you in heaven?
I must be strong
And carry on,
'Cause I know I don't belong
Here in heaven.

No Son Of Mine

Words & Music by Tony Banks, Phil Collins & Mike Rutherford.

1. Well the

key to my___ sur-vi -val   was ne-ver in much doubt,___

See block lyrics for Verses 2&3

he looked me straight in the eyes,_____ he said: You're no son,__ you're

no son__ of mine.____ You're no son,__ you're no son__ of mine.____

You walked out,__ you left us__ be-hind,____ and you're no son,__ you're

no son__ of mine._____

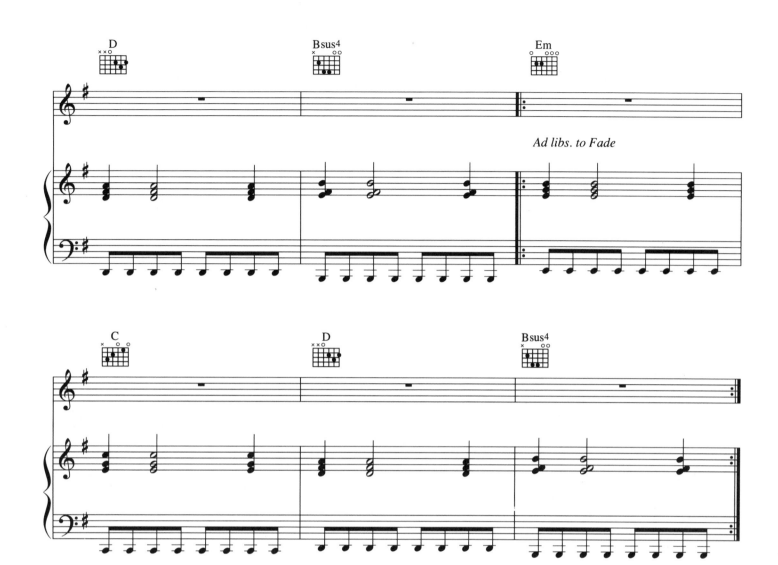

Ad libs. to Fade

Verse 2:
I didn't think much about it
'Til it started happening all the time.
Soon I was living with the fear every day
Of what might happen that night.
I couldn't stand to hear the crying
Of my mother, and I remember when
I swore that, that would be the last they'd see of me,
And I never went home again.

Verse 3: (D.S.)
Well the years passed so slowly,
I thought about him everyday,
What would I do if we passed on the street,
Would I keep running away?
In and out of hiding places,
Soon I'd have to face the facts,
That we'd have to sit down and talk it over,
And that would mean going back.

When You Tell Me That You Love Me

Words & Music by Albert Hammond & John Bettis.

dark when you tell me that you love ___ me.

(2.) I wan-na

love ___ me.

In a world with-out you,

I will al-ways hun-ger,

all I need is your love to make me strong ___ er.

cresc.

f

And ba - by

poco rall.

ev'-ry-time you touch me, I be-come a he-ro, I'll make you safe, no mat-ter where you

are. And bring you ev'-ry-thing you ask for, no-thing is a-bove me, I'm

shin-ing like a can-dle in the dark when you tell me that you love ___ me.

You love ___ me, when you tell me that you

love ___ me.

Crazy

Words & Music by Seal.

and through a frac-tal on a break-ing wall,____ I __ see you __ my friend __ and touch_your face__ a - gain._____ Mi - ra - cles__ will hap - pen as __ we speak.__ But we're ne-ver gon-na sur-vive _____ un - less we get a lit-tle__

VERSE 2:
Yellow people walking through my head
One of them's got a gun to shoot the other one
And yet together they were friends at school
(Yeah yeah yeah)
If I were there when we first took the pill
Then maybe . . .
Miracles will happen as we speak.

Rhythm Of My Heart

Words & Music by Marc Jordan & John Capek.

tongue. No, ne-ver will I roam for I know my place is home,__ where the

o - cean meets the sky I'll be sail - ing.

I'll__ be sail - ing

out __ there. __

The rhy-thm of my heart is beat-ing like a drum, the words "I love you" roll-ing off— my tongue.— Ne-ver will I roam— for I know my place is home.——— Where the o-cean meets the sky I'll be sail - ing.

rubato

Repeat to Fade

I Wonder Why

CURTIS STIGERS

Words & Music by Curtis Stigers & Glen Ballard.

al - ways con - vince me___ to stay, and I won-der why we

hold on with tears in our eyes and I won-der why we have to

break down to make things all right. And I won-der why I

can't seem to tell you good - bye,___ yeah I

won-der why.

1. 2. /F

I don't want to fight a -

D.S. ad lib. to Fade (Chorus 2)

VERSE 2:
Though I'm no angel
With my selfish pride,
But I love you more
Every day.
Love is an anger
That builds up inside
As the tears of frustration
Roll down my face.
Why does love always have to turn out
This way?

CHORUS 2:
And I wonder why we hold on
With tears in our eyes;
And I wonder why we have to break down
To just make things right;
And I wonder why I can't seem
To tell you goodbye,
Oh I wonder why.

Give Me Just A Little More Time

Words & Music by R. Dunbar & E. Wayne.

Verse 2:
You're young and you're in a hurry
You're eager for love but don't you worry;
We both want the sweetness in life
'Cause these things don't come overnight;
Don't give up 'cause love's been slow
Boy we're gonna succeed with another blow.

Verse 3:
Love is that mountain we must climb
Let's climb it together your hand in mine;
We haven't known each other too long
But the feeling I have is oh so strong;
I know we can make it, there's no doubt
We owe it to ourselves to find it out.

Goodnight Girl

Words & Music by Clarke, Cunningham, Mitchell & Pellow.

15495 5/93